The

Happiness

Handbook

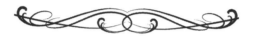

A User's Manual For
Living Your Extraordinary Life

A Workbook by

Jenn Flaa (and you)

The Happiness Handbook
Jenn Flaa

Copyright© 2012 Jennifer Flaa
ISBN Print 978-1-937445-22-5
ISBN Digital/EPub 978-1-937445-23-2
Library of Congress Control Number: 2012937049

The information in this book is provided for informational purposes only
and is not a substitute for professional advice. The author and publisher
make no legal claims, express or implied, and the material is not intended to
replace the services of a physician, psychologist, therapist, counselor, or
other qualified professional.

The author, publisher, and/or copyright holder assume no responsibility for
the loss or damage caused, or allegedly caused, directly or indirectly by the
use of information contained in this book. The author and publisher
specifically disclaim any liability incurred from the use or application of the
contents of this book.

Published by Bush Street Press
237 Kearny Street, #174
San Francisco, CA 94108
415-413-0785
Printed in the United States of America

Cover design by PixInk Design
Author Photo by Lori Fuller Photography

If I could have it any way
I wanted for myself,
this is how it would be ...

Table of Contents

Dedication	ix
Thanks	xi
Introduction	xiii
For the Guys	xv
The Juicy Gossip	17
How I Use this Book	19
What I Know for Sure – About Men	23
The Road to Happiness	27
How to Figure Out What Makes You Happy	45
What Makes Me Happy	51
What Makes Me Tick	65
Freaking Out	87
Who You (My Happiness Bringer) Are	91
Sex	97
The Dark Side	111
Living an Extraordinary Life	121
Life Purpose	125
Troubleshooting	127
Resources	151
About the Author	153
Staying in Touch	154
Index	155

Dedication

To all the guys who had to figure me out the hard way
... sorry about that.

Thanks

Many thanks to everyone who read the early versions, did the work and provided insightful comments and wisdom. I'm also very grateful to my friends who supported and encouraged me along the way and to the design, editing, layout and publishing team that helped bring my vision to life!

Big thanks (and a happy dance) to all the men who said, "Hurry up and publish this thing, we need to know how to make our girls happy!"

Special thanks to: John, Amy, Mark and Jessica Flaa, Janell Synstelien, Judy Froemke, Mary Anne Rasmussen, Aimee Lyndon-Adams, Deborah Lynne Lombardo, Nandini Rao, Barbara Grace Pike, Joyce Arnowitz, Keren Peled, Lori Fuller, Barbara Avitan, Maureen Molloy, Ayesha Mathews-Wadhwa, Stephanie Vozza, Linda Eskridge Alicia Dunams and to the amazing man who is my peace.

Introduction

When my nieces and nephews were born, they arrived in the usual manner: totally naked and without instructions. We all had to get used to each other and learn what each little sound, move and cry meant.

Just think how much easier it would be for new parents to read *"a long, sustained wail with the relative pitch of G# means I'm hungry,"* and *"wet dog noses on my tummy make me giggle."*

Clearly none of us arrive on the planet with a user's manual about what makes us tick as individuals or click as friends and lovers. We have to figure this out by trial and error (a lot of error). And each new friend and dating partner has to figure us out ... again, mostly by error.

But what if we changed the rules? What if we wrote our own user's manual and gave it to the people we love most (or at least to the people who need to read it the most)? Imagine how that could change our interactions and our lives. People would begin to do what makes us happy and ... we would *be* happy! If someone received the user's manual and chose not to follow it, well then, we could choose not to hang out with them more quickly.

This workbook came about after my divorce; I decided that my only task in life now was to be happy. But coming from a place of sorrow, despair and, in general, being "broken," I discovered that happiness was a process for me, not a moment. It took time for me to remember and fantasize about what makes me happy, more time to implement it, and even more time to learn to really soak it in and receive it.

When I started dating again, I noticed three things:

1. It was really clear that the guys wanted to make me happy and do things that pleased me.

2. It made me happy to see their smiles when they got it right.

3. Mistakes in happiness actions were being made accidentally.

   - Flowers? Good. Carnations? BAD.

   - Making out? Good. While in line at the market? Not so much.

Around this time, I also started a new band and decided to be very clear right from the start. So, I wrote down my lists and talked about how I work, how I handle upset and my "dark side." The response was really positive and … I was happy! So I continued to refine the lists, add more lists and talk about them to the people who needed to know these things about me.

Then a sweet, sexy man showed up … and I added the spicy sections.

Am I happy now? Teehehehehehee, oh, yes! I actually walk around some days and think, "Geez, I'm really happy!" What a welcome change this is.

And now it's your turn! Enjoy receiving life … just how you want it for yourself.

For the Guys

One of the things that guys ask me *a lot* is, "How do I make a woman happy?" When I tell them I wrote this book, they get really happy because—voila!—they think they'll now have the answers.

Nope, sorry guys, it's not quite that easy. There's not one thing that makes us all happy. We're all unique (in fact, that's what you love about us, right?!) So, what works for one lovely chica ... might turn another one completely off!

But here's how you can use this book to help figure it out:

1. Throughout this book, in the sidebars, women have answered the question: "What makes me happy is ____." What I want you to notice is the general theme; it's easy stuff to provide and usually free. We lead busy and stressful lives these days and have to do so much for so many. It often makes us happy to get a moment where we can stop and savor a simple pleasure.

2. Use the topics in this book as conversation starters with your girl. Bonus points if you take notes and actually do the stuff later!

3. Do the book yourself and tell us girls what makes *you* happy. Because it makes us happy to make you happy! Happy men are soooo gorgeous and compelling!

The Juicy Gossip/My Story

It seems like everyone these days is dishing out their "stuff" for a world of strangers to see, and books like these always include a section about the author's story ... so here is mine:

I was born and then crap happened. Really crappy stuff. Stuff that's hard to forgive. Stuff that would justify me being mad, unhappy, even depressed for the rest of my life.

"Oooh, what were those events?" you may say.

Well, here's where I differ from the disclose-all fad of the day. What happened isn't stuff I share with people – even close friends who have known me for years. I have to live with those old movies in my head. I don't want you to look at me and see those movies, too.

I am more than those events. They shaped my life, and I've moved on. I'm happy now. It doesn't make me happy to talk about that ancient history, and I'm all about being happy!

You've had crap happen to you, too. Maybe it's the same crap as me, maybe it's worse. Or maybe it's not, but it still shook you up. That's valid, too.

In an old Native American story, a grandfather explains to his grandson that there are two wolves doing battle inside of him. One wolf is unforgiving, mean and unhappy, and the other wolf is compassionate, friendly and happy. The grandson's eyes widen, and he asks which wolf will win. "The one I feed," replies the grandfather.

I believe what you talk about stays alive. You feed it and give it energy, not allowing the experience to become neutral and fade away.

This book (and my story) isn't a tell-all, dredging up the old stuff, dwelling on it and feeling justified in being unhappy because crap happened to me.

This is about moving beyond that. I did it and you can, too, even if you're really unhappy right now.

No one can tell you how to be happy. What makes you happy is different from what makes anyone else happy. But there is a path we can all take, a journey of self-discovery to find your happiness. I know the way. I'll be your Sherpa. I'll gently guide you as you make your way from unhappy to neutral to happy.

Come on! Let's start the journey!

How I Use this Book

I've been using my version of this book since 2008, and it's been a great guide through new relationships and through trouble spots in existing relationships. Here's how I've used the book:

Overcoming Heartbreak

Awhile back, I was madly in love with a guy and incredibly happy ... until he spiraled out of control with an addiction issue. My emotional roller coaster plummeted me from a happy high peak to the depths of despair. I remember while I was in my off-the-charts sorrow phase I thought, *"I should pull out my happiness book and do some of the things that make me happy."* But it wasn't the right time yet. My experience was such a shocking blow that I needed a little more time to let the sorrow run its course, instead of stuffing it and moving on. (In my experience, if I don't work it out, it will pop up again when I least expect and want it!)

I'm sure I wasn't fun to be around, but I needed time. Eventually, I came back to the book, used some of the techniques in the Troubleshooting section (like "The Chair" and "At Bat") and started being my own happiness provider until I turned the corner and was genuinely happy again.

This book helps me focus and get back to happiness when an unhappy event occurs!

The Top Five Deal Breakers

When I start dating someone new, I watch to see if they naturally are in alignment with my Top Five Deal Breakers. Once I told a guy, "I'd really like monogamy," and he said, "I'd love it if *you* were monogamous." After delving into that turn of a phrase, it was clear he wouldn't love it if *he* were monogamous. So we ended it as friends before other women got involved!

After the addiction debacle, I added that to my Top Five Deal Breakers, tipping the scale for me at six, though! Lucky I did. Not long after, I was dating a fun man who lived in the Pacific Northwest. Everything was going great, and he invited my dog, Miss Sophie, and me to spend the summer with him. We'd rent a houseboat; it'd be awesome. I was really excited but I came back to my Top Five ... ahh, Six. He had no problem with the first five, but when we got to the addiction discussion and I shared my story and said that I never, ever wanted to go through that again, he admitted that he loved beer a little too much. And he kindly bowed out.

I could think he chose beer over me, but he's a good man. I believe he was providing me happiness by stepping out and allowing someone else who could naturally give me my Top Six to step in.

Trouble Spots & Red Flags

I have one relationship in my life that feels like we're on different planets. Communication is tricky and feelings get hurt ... often. So, I come back to what makes me happy and communicate that. I use it as a boundary-setting tool; if they violate it, I let them know and then go away for a while. It might mean taking a walk, and it might mean having more space between the times we're in contact. As I'm aging, I don't have patience for people who know what makes me happy and choose to ignore or do the opposite. That's a red flag for me.

I wasn't good with boundaries until I started looking at it as "bringing," "withholding" or even "taking" happiness.

The Action of "Being" Happy

Finally, I thought a lot about how happiness "looks" in my body. Am I smiling and playful in my attitude and in my language? Am I happy dancing when happiness "bringing" occurs, and am I using the words, "I'm happy"?

When I started this book, I wasn't. There really wasn't an outward sign that I was happy (more on this coming up). Now I'm aware of how happiness shows up in my body and just how much that affects others ... and makes them happy.

Love that!

What I Know for Sure – About Men

Of this I am certain, most normal, healthy men are hardwired to make women happy. When they get it right, all is well in their world and they feel like winners ... and that translates to everything they do.

If they get it wrong or don't get any feedback that they succeeded in delivering happiness, that disappointment, dejection and futility translates to the rest of their world. They feel like the opposite of a winner – a loser – and that's a big deal for them.

What that Means for Us Chicas

If you take the premise that men want to make us happy and need feedback that they got it right, that means we have only three responsibilities in our relationships:

1. **Decide** what makes us happy.
2. **Communicate** that clearly and precisely to the other person(s).
3. **Happy dance** when they get it right. Men are visual and a happy dance speaks louder than words. That little shaking of your booty actually breaks through and signals the inner cortex of "man brain" and rings the "I'm a winner" bell for them!

The One Thing I Want You to Know

This next story is huge, a big peek into the male psyche. I hope it provides you with the insight and an a-ha moment that helps you understand the "man brain" and gives you the motivation to work the three steps above (Decide, Communicate, Happy Dance) so that you can provide your sweetie with this amazing gift!!

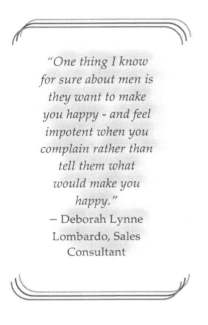

"One thing I know for sure about men is they want to make you happy - and feel impotent when you complain rather than tell them what would make you happy."
— Deborah Lynne Lombardo, Sales Consultant

Once upon a time, a spunky young rocker/aspiring author had some construction done in her back yard. Yes, hot, sweaty men doing manual labor. At the end of a hard day, she appeared; one of the workers looked at her while gesturing to the completed work and said, "Are you happy?"

Are you happy?

Not, "Do you like it?" Or, "How'd I do?" But, "Are you happy?"

Hmm, that's interesting, she noted. Then she proceeded to "ooh and ahh" over the work, to comment on the little details she noticed and to do a little happy dance, smile and sparkle a bit.

"Thank you," the man said. "Your smile gives me energy."

Your smile gives me energy.

A tear came to my eye – yes ... of course, the story is mine – and I got it. I really got the gift that we give men.

Do you get it too? Our smile gives them energy.

Great! Now work this book and the three steps (Decide, Communicate, Happy Dance) so you can give this extraordinary gift to the fellas around you. And how ironic is it that we give this gift by receiving!

Many of us work hard to pay attention to what everyone else needs and wants, and what makes them happy, and sometimes it feels selfish for us to be happy. It's time to reframe that old belief!

The truth is, when we are happy, we are still giving.

We give to others by allowing ourselves to receive. Our happiness and our smiles give them energy.

The Road to Happiness

*T*he *Happiness Handbook* is your personal user's manual, a tool to facilitate your own journey and to help you communicate with your loved one(s). On the following pages, I've listed several categories for you to define what makes you happy – whether you are alone or with a partner. Each section has introductory remarks and an example or two. I've included blank pages where you can write lists and stories about what makes you happy. If you are reading this book on an electronic device, consider creating your own Happiness Handbook Journal where you can easily write and share your answers. Don't freak out about the "homework" … I've also got some instructions for how to figure out what makes you happy, as well as troubleshooting techniques if you get stuck or are starting from a place of being really unhappy.

A Word on Terminology

I use the term "happiness bringer" to identify the person who provides that which makes you happy (sometimes it's yourself). Some folks may get upset about using the terms "makes you happy" and "happiness bringer" as if this takes away someone's power or implies that they *need* someone else to make them happy. That's not what I mean at all.

Happiness is a choice – *your* choice. Each person needs to know what instills happiness inside of them. Once you know what makes you happy, you can communicate that to others so they can more fully participate in the enrichment of your life.

> "What makes me happy is a walk in the park, a massage, a good book/movie, an unexpected act of kindness, good conversations with friends, and fun things with my girl friends, especially when they drive miles to spend time with me."
> – Nandini Rao, Technical Writer

For example, if getting flowers makes you happy, you'll need someone to be the "bringer" of the flowers. You're still in your power. You defined it, and you received it. None of that diminished you or made you *need* the flower bringer in an unhealthy manner. In fact, the exchange was probably circular and complete. When you received the flowers, smiled, inhaled their scent and said "thanks," the flower bringer received a moment of feeling good; he or she succeeded in providing you with a happy moment. (You are also free to bring yourself flowers and still do the happy dance!)

I'll make a deal with you. If those terms really push your buttons, feel free to cross them out and write in something else. I'm OK with that. Whatever makes you happy works for me.

The Three Steps of Happiness

Before we dive into what makes you happy, let's explore each of the three steps you'll be taking on your journey to happiness. Remember, we said they were to:

1. **Decide** what makes you happy

2. **Communicate** clearly and precisely

3. **Happy Dance**

STEP 1: Decide What Makes You Happy

Let's assume, for the moment, that you are currently not at your happiest. Sitting down and saying, "What makes me happy is x, y and z," may feel unachievable or foreign. I remember when I was so sad that thinking about what makes me happy actually made me cry. I'd had happiness once and it got ripped away; it just didn't feel like I could ever get there again.

Deep breath, please. We're going to aim a little lower at first. You are currently experiencing a "happiness deficit." It's OK, it's normal and it's curable!

The Happiness Deficit

When you are just plain unhappy or at a loss for where to start to "be happy," you may have a happiness deficit. You could be so unhappy that you'll first need to take a look at what will get you to neutral before you can focus on happy-making things.

If your basic human needs are not being met for whatever reason, it will be nearly impossible for you to get to "happy." For example, if you hadn't eaten in four days and someone gave you flowers, you'd probably think, "That's nice, but how about a sandwich?!"

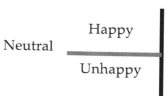

If you can relate and feel like you're in a happiness deficit, then skip ahead and start with the *What Makes Me Tick* section. That section focuses on your basic needs. You can use the *How To Figure Out What Makes Me Happy* section as a resource. Once you've got that figured out, come back to *What Makes Me Happy* and try figuring out that section.

If you're like me, you may need to have your basic needs met for a while before you can take a breath and dream about what actual happiness would be like! This is what I meant when

I said that happiness could be a process. For some of us, it takes time and that's OK.

Forgiveness

Ironically, when someone hurts you, the first thing other people often say is, "Oh, you need to forgive him or her." Excuse me? Really? Shouldn't the first step be for the perpetrator of unhappiness or hurt to say he or she is sorry? I'm just saying!

With that little venting out of the way, we can get back to the platitude that "forgiveness is the gift you give yourself." It also ties in nicely with my theory of not feeding "the crap" that happened to you. Once you forgive someone, your brain lets it go –and you don't dwell on it so much anymore. So, you feel better and move on with your life and allow happiness to seep back into your mind, heart and bones.

OK, that's the goal. But I'm pretty sure we all agree that sometimes reaching a goal takes practice or a little work!

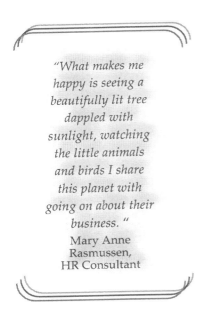

"What makes me happy is seeing a beautifully lit tree dappled with sunlight, watching the little animals and birds I share this planet with going on about their business."

Mary Anne Rasmussen, HR Consultant

Here's where I think "forgiveness" goes sideways these days. I have a friend who was married for 20 years to a person who suffered from bipolar disease (manic depression). Her life would be going great, he'd go off his meds and life would spiral out of control. He'd ask for forgiveness, she'd take him back and eventually this cycle just kept happening over and over again.

At one point, near the end of their marriage, they were in therapy together and the therapist asked her if she could forgive him for ALL 20 years of crap, right there, right now. Just do it … bam!

Clearly, this "therapist" was clueless. Those of us who have been *really, deeply* hurt know that forgiveness doesn't happen in an instant. It's a process and often starts with the statement, "one day, I may be willing to forgive." That's enough to get you started down the road.

Forgiveness may be a byproduct of your work in this book. That'd be cool. Just don't put too much pressure on yourself and think that forgiveness must come before happiness. Boy, that would be terrible if we all had to wait for that! Nope, just work on the happiness and allow yourself to one day be willing to forgive. Just that little bit can help soften your heart and mind enough to allow you to explore what being happy might look like again.

And please, always remember, you are not alone. So many of us have wrestled with how to forgive people who have made bad choices. And sometimes, we have to learn how to forgive ourselves, too.

Defining Happiness in Terms of Others

As I "tested" this book, I found that many people defined their happiness by focusing on others; what makes someone else happy.

For example, what makes me happy is:

- *"Cooking the foods **you** like"* or
- *"Keeping the house clean for **you**"*

It's true we can find happiness by making others happy, but I'd like to encourage you to think a little more selfishly.

Defining what makes you and you alone happy doesn't mean that you are a selfish person. In this exercise, I give you permission to think just about yourself and what pleases you for a few moments. Need a jumpstart? What about the simple things like these:

What makes me happy is:

- A gentle breeze on my face

- The sun on my back as I lay on the sand at the beach

- Shopping for a new outfit

- Receiving flowers

- Eating chocolate

- Being organized so I can find things right away

- Reading a good book

- Watching my favorite show

While working through these exercises, keep in mind the construction story from the previous chapter. When we're happy, it gives them energy and it makes them happy. So, a little foray into "selfishness" is a good thing and worthy of experimenting with! (By the way, did you notice how many things in my list above were things that I can provide for myself, being my own happiness bringer?)

The Happiness Layer Cake

 When I started to write this book, I brainstormed my big list of what makes me happy, with no categories, priorities or organization (yet). Upon closer look, I realized there were basically three layers – like a three-tiered cake – and there was an order of priority.

The bottom layer, the foundation, is the absolute basics we don't want to live without; the stuff you'll write down in the *Top Five Must Haves* section. You'll find that many of these things are things that you provide for yourself, like food, water or enough sleep.

The middle layer is filled with the things that people do; the qualities in people that make you love to be around them. Here are a few examples from my list:

- Having integrity

- Being honest

- Being a cheerleader that supports and encourages me

- Paying attention and helping me out – seeing what needs to be done and jumping in and doing it

- Being a gentleman, i.e., opening doors and attentiveness

The top layer is made up of the things you like to do together as well as by yourself. Here are a few examples from my list:

- Singing

- Going to the theatre, symphony, concerts and clubs to hear live music

- Starting and completing projects (not so much the middle part)

- Playing "the best part of the day" game before bed

What's "the best part of the day" game? Ooh, I love this. Ask each other, "What was the best part of your day?" It gives you a moment of reflection over your day and a chance to share the best part. You end your day on a positive note. Plus, I gotta tell ya, when they respond authentically with, "being here with you right now," boy does that feel good!

That should give you a context for starting your own lists. Remember, if you're stuck, flip to the Troubleshooting and Resources sections. There are lots of exercises that help you with "writer's block" or to move through anger and resentment and get to neutral and beyond.

STEP 2: Communicating What Makes You Happy

Once you've figured out what makes you happy, the next step is to either provide that for yourself, if you're in an alone phase of your life, or communicate it to others.

What I Know for Sure – Mind Reading

It's not good enough to just figure out what makes you happy ... you actually have to tell people! I know for sure that 99.99% of people do not read minds. Do you read your loved one's minds? See, I didn't think so. Why do we think they can read ours? It's a funny little trap so many of us fall into. "If you really loved me ... you'd just know." Hello ... Santa loves us and we still write him a letter and spell out exactly what would make us happy! (Um ... when we were kids!)

Hints

Hints don't work, either. Men are pretty easy to work with when you figure this one out. If you tell them something, they tend to do it. If you hint, they tend to mess it up. In general, girls get hints and boys don't. Boys respond to clarity. They want to get it right, so tell them exactly what "right" is so that their aim is on target. Think sports; they need to see the hoop, goal line, and home plate. When they see that, they can win!

> "One thing I know for sure about men is they love to be recognized and appreciated (a little ego-stroking goes a long way)."
> – Lana Goldenberg, President at Lana Goldenberg & Associates

When you spell it out for them, it doesn't mean that they are stupid. Making you happy is the new game in town. Tell them the rules, show them the goal, and get out of the way so they can win!

Timing Is Everything

Rule 1: Don't Overwhelm

You're so excited; you just worked on this book and figured out what makes you happy in all the categories. So, wham, you pop it down into your sweetie's lap. Whoa, poor fella.

"What makes me happy is characters and objects of beauty." – Ayesha Mathews-Wadhwa, CEO of PixInk Design

There's so much information, where should he begin? And he'll probably wonder if this means he's done it all wrong and now you are "correcting" him. (Which tends to make guys want to NOT do it!)

There's a much more gentle and effective way.

Tip 1: Don't give him the list yet, but start happy dancing when he accidentally gets stuff right. He's probably been with you for a while and has paid attention. Odds are he'll get a few things right. Remember though, you may have shut him down (like I did when I was married) by not having a happy dance when he got it right in the past.

Tip 2: Start with one section. Make it an easy one where he's already getting a lot right. "Look honey, I did this happiness book and I'm so happy to find out that you're already doing a lot of stuff that makes me happy!" <Insert smile or happy dance here.> He may start asking what else makes you happy.

Tip 3: Watch for natural places in life that you can insert a "happiness statement." For example, if he was leaving for the store to pick up eggs, you could say, "Oooh, you know it'd make me really happy if you brought some raspberries. I just love them." Then do the little dance when he remembers it. If he forgets, don't make a big deal out of it; he's still learning.

Of course, it's got to be something that actually makes you happy. Telling him that bringing home the paper towels would make you happy …that's a little…weird. (Well…unless there's another use for paper towels I'm not aware of!)

One of my friends is in her 60s and she'd never spent a moment thinking about what makes her happy. She's a very loving person and always focused on making others happy. She sat in on one of my talks and did the exercise to brainstorm a list of 13 things that made her happy (lucky #13)! She went home and gave her sweetie the list and – wham! – within days he'd done six of them. (Yes, she happy danced, too!) She called me three days later in tears; so grateful that she'd had an opportunity to figure it out and have a tool or mechanism to convey it to the man she's deeply in love with.

> "One thing I know for sure about men is that they are easy to please and eager to please."
> – Nandini Rao, Technical Writer

Rule 2: Watch the Focus

You may have noticed that men are really good at focusing on one thing at time. This is great because when they are focused on us, we have their utter and complete attention.

What we need to pay attention to is when they are *not* focused on us, so we don't tell them things or ask them to do things while they are focused on something else. This, accidently, sets them up for failure and they are unable to "win."

This is important. Remember, they want to "win" at making us happy, so we need to give them a fighting chance at it.

Here's what it's like for them: What if Sam was rushing to catch an airplane to Atlanta, and his sweetie, Sally, yelled, "It'd make me happy to go to New York for my birthday in six months." Now Sally is thinking, "Cool, I've told Sam what makes me happy and given him plenty of time to plan it. This is going to be a great birthday." Nope, all Sam was thinking was "catch the plane, catch the plane, catch the plane." At some point he may think, "Huh, what was that about New York?" But he won't even remember who said "New York" let alone in what context.

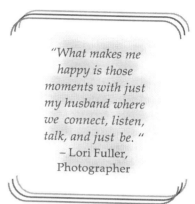

"What makes me happy is those moments with just my husband where we connect, listen, talk, and just be. "
– Lori Fuller, Photographer

Rule 3: It's In His Eyes

How do you know you have his attention? Remember when you were dating? He'd look into your eyes and drink in everything about you. He was paying really close attention to what made you happy. So, if he's not looking at you ... forget it. You do not have his focus.

Now, you could get hurt or you could just train yourself to speak:

- Clearly

- Concisely (get to the point; think short attention span – it's not a bad thing—it just is)

- Only when you have his focus

Seriously, if you were a guy, wouldn't you want a woman who "got you" and set you up to win? That's not manipulation – it's basketball – handing off the ball to your teammate so they can score and you (both) can win.

Are You Mystery Dating?

There are a couple sections that are just gold for you (no, not the sex part just yet). *What Makes Me Tick* and *Who You (My Happiness Bringer) Are* sections can help you sift through the dating rabble a bit faster. Once you know someone is meeting your basic needs and that they have the minimum characteristics you require in a sweetie, you can start sharing the *What Makes Me Happy* sections and eventually ... other sections, too.

"One thing I know for sure about men is that they need to make a difference. In the world or just in their lover's world, they need to be significant."
– Mary Anne Rasmussen, HR Consultant

Probably not a good idea to lay it all on them on the first date, or even all at once. Take your time. A little mystery never hurt and it's always nice to leave them wanting more!

OK, caveat here: I'm divorced and still dating, so clearly I have no handle on this! Hehhhehe

Are You in a Relationship?

Give it a try. See if defining and communicating your needs and desires adds a little spark to your relationship.

What if it doesn't? Your relationship is still where it was, but now you've got some clarity. The rest is up to you. There are resources in your Yellow Pages and Google for counseling and facilitating change if you want some help.

Communicating with Family and Friends

You can use sections of this workbook to help initiate conversation with your family and friends. Of course, you'll want to edit certain sections. Personally, I can't imagine sharing the spicy sections with anyone other than my sweetie.

STEP 3: Happy Dance

When I was married, my husband gave me a wonderful anniversary present. On a sunny warm weekend, we stayed along the Sonoma coast and hiked, camped, spent a night in a cute little bed and breakfast, ate amazing meals and capped it all off with an Eric Clapton concert at Oakland Arena with *really* good seats. The whole anniversary "event" was so fun and memorable, just perfect, and yes, made me happy.

But during our (amicable) divorce process he said, "Did that trip even make you happy?"

WHAT!!!??? How could he not have known? Where did that snafu?

Thank heavens he said that because it really got me thinking about how I communicate what makes me happy and how I receive it. Clearly I was doing something wrong!

That's when I realized that saying "thank you" (vertically or horizontally) isn't enough. There needs to be a more immediate, visible and visceral connection to get through "man brain." And once I understood that … the fun really began!

The Face of Happiness

Now take a moment to think about how you look and behave when you are happy.

How does happiness show up in your body? How would the bringer of happiness know that they did a good job?

This exercise may coax you into behavior changes. That's how it worked for me. When I reflected on this, I realized that in the past, most happy-making events were a surprise. So, I responded with shock and disbelief, but to the happiness bringer, I appeared stoic. If a gift was involved, I'd squirrel it away because it was a precious treasure. To the gift bringer, it looked as

though I didn't like it and was hiding it away.

After contemplating this topic, I realized my behavior didn't encourage the happiness bringer to repeat the action or take another risk to solicit happiness. No wonder I was so surprised when it happened!

How about you? Do you smile, squeal or giggle? Do you gush profuse praise? Do you sit or stand in an open, receptive posture (i.e.: not crossing your arms or legs)? Do you take a deep breath and soak it all in? I recommend trying this one, it feels really good.

What about a happy dance? Do you have a happy dance? Do you let the happiness tingle and energize your whole body? What's a happy dance, you ask? It's pretty much however you choose to shake your booty. Mine is kind of the Tom Cruise, *Risky Business* slide across the kitchen floor with shaking and hoopin' and hollerin.' (Except I usually leave my pants on.) Go on; give it a try when no one's watching … you know you want to!

A happy dance may not feel "authentic" and "real" to you (yet). So, start small and keep paying attention to the response it has in the other person and how the feeling changes in your body as you let the happiness seep through to all your cells! Before you know it, you'll have a booty-shaking version of your own happy dance!

You may not want to do the full on happy dance at the meat counter of the local grocery when the fella hands you a steak, so, feel free to explore a couple different varieties for different occasions!

Happiness as Manipulation

As I was telling people about this book, I received a response from a woman that threw me for a loop. She said, "Yes, but if I tell him [her husband] what makes me happy, what will I have to hold over him?" I went mute and gave her my deer-in-the-headlights look as my brain struggled to comprehend what she had just said. Luckily, she continued on with her explanation. "If I don't tell him what makes me happy then he'll keep trying. I'm afraid that if I tell him what makes me happy, he'll stop trying. I won't be a challenge anymore." I asked her how her marriage was and if she was happy; she replied "strained" and "no." I don't think her strategy is working for her.

People need positive reinforcement. They need to know they are succeeding or winning at the opportunity to please you. I know I need it.

> "One thing I know for sure about men is they need us more than we need them!"
> – Alicia Dunams, Publisher and Speaker

Here's how happiness bringing went awry for me in the past. I once had a boyfriend. Wait ... let me rephrase that so I don't sound like a complete loser ... I had this one boyfriend for whom I once went all out on his birthday. I planned for weeks, cooked for days and took him on an amazing, romantic trip filled with lots of little touches and his favorite things. His response? He gave me the deer-in-the-headlights look, left and went for a walk. What! I was shocked ... and alone in the room. Turns out, no one had ever paid attention to what he liked and gave him a gift like that before. He was so shocked; he didn't know how to receive this gift.

And my response? OK, let me just say that I wasn't the most mature person on the planet. I had done so much work for him; to have him not take it in, smile, say "thanks," and do a happy dance or some other juicy gratitude action, really hurt my feelings. Did I ever do anything like that for him again? Oh, honey, please … you've got to be kidding!

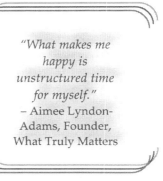

"What makes me happy is unstructured time for myself."
– Aimee Lyndon-Adams, Founder, What Truly Matters

The whole relationship began to unravel for me from that point. I swooped down into a happiness deficit and it became more difficult for him to make me happy. Remember, I fessed up to not handling this maturely. Would I do better now? Let's hope I don't have to find out!

If you are withholding happiness from yourself for any reason, consider this:

- What benefit are you getting (or do you think you're getting) by withholding your own happiness?
- Is that a bigger payoff than actually being happy would be?
- Which makes you happy: having your sweetie "try" harder or having your sweetie actually "do" the right happy-making actions?

I'd like to encourage you to do a little experiment. You do NOT have to change. I'm not asking for that. I'm just asking you to conduct your own experiment and see how it goes for you. If the results are positive, you can draw your own conclusions about whether or not changing your mind (and your behavior) would be a good thing for you.

An Experiment

Start paying close attention the next time your happiness bringer does something to make you happy; instead of withholding your happy response, bring it on. It doesn't have to be big, grand, gushing or dramatic. Authentic is good, really good, in fact. Just remembering to say "thank you" is good. Maybe add in a deep, receptive breath or a "you're so thoughtful." Better yet, name it, "Thanks, ___*blah blah*___ makes me happy."

Now, keep paying attention. Does your happiness bringer cease all happy-making actions? Or did their face light up and did they continue more happy-making actions? (I'm laying money down on this result for you.)

If you've been withholding your happiness, your happiness bringer may now be in a state of shock. So, don't stop the experiment. Try it a couple more times and watch their response. Who knows, by continuing the experiment, you may just be softly implementing a relatively painless, happiness-receiving behavior for yourself.

How to Figure Out What Makes You Happy

Here are some techniques I've used to mine my brain for what makes me happy. Use the ones that appeal to you and disregard the rest.

We're about to dive in and create your lists. You may want to write down everything you can think of and then divvy it up into the appropriate sections later. It might be easier to think of all the things that make you happy first, and then pick your top five or put them into the various categories.

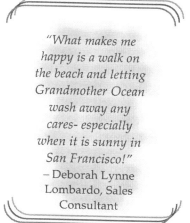

"What makes me happy is a walk on the beach and letting Grandmother Ocean wash away any cares- especially when it is sunny in San Francisco!"
– Deborah Lynne Lombardo, Sales Consultant

Techniques for Figuring Out What Makes You Happy

There are a couple different methods you can use for determining exactly what makes you happy:

Meditation

Find a quiet spot where you won't be disturbed. Take several deep breaths, and relax your body and your mind. If you have a meditation practice, you can do that. If not (and you want one), you can refer to the *Resources* section in the back of the book.

Free Association Writing

Just start writing. For example, if the topic is happiness, just start writing about happiness. Anything you can think of. Don't worry about spelling or grammar or making sense or putting it in any kind of order. Don't worry if it's positive or negative. Don't judge it; just write. Come back in a day or two and organize it.

> "What makes me happy is dancing, getting stuff done, when my man does what he says he would do, spas, spending time with friends and family, spending time with the man I love, when the man I love shows me he's thinking about me."
> – Keren Peled, Jewelry Designer

Let go of the fact that it's got to be right the first time you write it down. Let me tell you a little secret: I used to think people wrote songs and books, starting at the beginning and ending at the end. Not so. For many of us creative types, ideas pop in but usually not in the "right" order. Some ideas are never used; they are bridges to another thought or a better way of saying something.

Often when I write a song, I just start free writing. At a certain point, I'll have several pages and I'll go circle all of the cool turns of a phrase; it's like putting a puzzle together to figure out the order. Sometimes the song I intended to write never gets written and something else is the result (it's how this book was born). Give yourself permission to be "messy." You can organize and prioritize it later!

Remember, you are on a journey and some parts of the trail are going to be muddy!

Brainstorm

Sometimes you need another brain on the job. Call a friend, have a cup of coffee or a drink, and start brainstorming together. Share all your ideas, even the loopy, wild ones! Brainstorming can be quite fun; the things you say will trigger ideas in your friend. Be sure someone takes notes or record the conversation. An added benefit; you'll get to learn new and interesting things about your friend!

"What makes me happy is a long walk aside the river, with my dog."
– Annette Frey, CEO of Biscuits By Lampchop.

You'll find many of my friends' happiness items scattered throughout this book. It may trigger an idea in you. Either, "Oh yeah, that makes me happy too!" or "No way ... but hey, this similar (or opposite) thing makes me happy."

Walking

Stop working on this and go take a walk. Taking the pressure off and enjoying nature or your neighborhood can often spark new ideas. If it doesn't work for you, come walk my dog. Maybe it's the dog that's the important element!

Reminisce and Fantasize

Spend some time thinking about how you were in the past. Is there anything you want to revive?

Find some alone time. Turn off the computer and phone, and get comfortable. Perhaps you'll want to be outside or lying down. Now just let your mind wander over past events that made you happy. If you fall asleep, no worries; you may get some clues in your dreams. Try to only focus on the things that made you happy. Don't take the story to the conclusion, where the jerk messed up and you broke up. Just recall the happy moments. (Also see the *Getting Unstuck – Getting To Neutral* section in the *Troubleshooting* section and the "Cut the Link" exercise in the *Troubleshooting* section.)

Then fantasize about the future. How will you be then? How would you want it to be if you could have it exactly the way you want for yourself?

Opposites

Many of us collect our life data by using the "nope, that's not it" model. If that's you, put it to work for you. Write down all the things that didn't work in one column, and add a second column for its opposite. That might help you narrow in on what will work for you. Have fun with it, and get it all out. That'll help make a space for what you do like and what makes you happy.

"One thing I know for sure about men is that they way more sensitive than (most) will ever want us to know."
– Kari Wishingrad, Actor

I recommend focusing on the positive, the things that do make you happy. Here's why: Let's say you write,

*"I like chocolate but getting Hershey chocolate on Valentine's Day really **doesn't** make me happy."*

When your loved one goes to buy you a Valentine's present, they will say to themselves,

"Oh yes, chocolate is a win. What kind was it? Yes, I remember reading about Hershey. Hershey it is then."

So, your loved one remembered … but not quite perfectly. So, mention mostly what you do like. As an added bonus, thinking about positive things that make you happy might just make you feel happy right now.

Organizing Your Happiness Lists

Random or Priority Order?

Many people imply an order when they see a numbered list, with #1 being the most important. Some people write numbered lists in the order something popped into their head. Please note which rule of thumb you are using. This detail will help the people with whom you share your Happiness Handbook— your user's manual. (For example: I tend to brainstorm the list; the reader might assume the first item is the most important when it really was just the first thing that popped into my head. If you're like that, let your reader know.)

> "What makes me happy is experiencing new food, laughing with loved ones, being by the water, giving a thoughtful gift, and being creative."
> – Grace Kang, Owner, Pink Olive Boutique

Add Your Stories

You may want to add a few stories to support some of your items. Stories help people remember and give them insight into why your preferences came to be.

For example: One of the occasional cheats I like in the summer is green, mint chip ice cream. I eat a very healthy diet so this is way out of context for me, but it's actually a comfort food from my childhood. I used to sit at the Formica kitchen table with my grandparents. We'd each have a bowl of mint chip ice cream, and we'd play with it and wait until it was melted enough to swirl around before we'd eat it. I felt warm and loved and blissfully playful, and I like recalling that memory and feeling. I bet you have similar stories; they will help your happiness bringer feel closer to you and understand that it's more than just "green ice cream" they are bringing you!

What Makes Me Happy

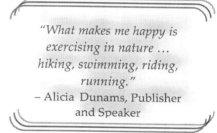

Now it's your turn. On the following pages are several sections and worksheets for you to write down your lists of what makes you happy. They are organized as follows:

- What Makes Me Happy
- What Makes Me Tick
- Freaking Out
- Who Your Happiness Bringer Is
- Sex
- The Dark Side
- Living Your Extraordinary Life

> *"What makes me happy is exercising in nature ... hiking, swimming, riding, running."*
> – Alicia Dunams, Publisher and Speaker

You can take as little or as long as you like to complete your *Happiness Handbook.*

Please be gentle with yourself when you begin to implement it. It may take practice to ask for things you need and want. If you're not used to being an active receiver, it will take practice to remember to say "thank you," smile or do the happy dance. It's OK. Rome wasn't built in a day, and neither were you. Let the changes you desire be gentle. Try not to be hard on yourself if you forget to ask for what you need or if you forget to receive graciously. Tomorrow is another day and another opportunity to try again.

If you get stuck, take a breath, relax and turn to the *Troubleshooting* and *Resources* sections in the back for help.

Have fun!

What Makes Me Happy –
My Top Five Must Haves

These are the top five things that make me happy. I don't want to live without them. They give me juice and energy and make life so much better by having them.

Example: You looking at me with soft eyes.

_____

_____

_____

_____

_____

_____

_____

_____

_____

What Happiness Looks Like On Me

This is how I look and behave when I'm happy.

Example: I smile.

_____

_____

_____

_____

_____

_____

_____

_____

_____

_____

The Things You Do that Make Me Happy

These are the things you do or the qualities you have that make me happy.

Example: Helping me out; you see things that need to be done and jump in and do them without my having to ask. Boy is that ever a relief!

_____

_____

_____

_____

_____

_____

_____

_____

_____

The Things We Do that Make Me Happy

These are the things we do together or I do by myself that make me happy.

Example: I like to go to a Giants baseball game once or twice a summer. I love taking the ferry, sitting in the sun, eating "bad" food and watching the game. I've done this since I was four years old, and it brings back very fond memories. I like it when you ask me about these memories so I can have the happiness of reliving them as we make new ones together. If no one is available to go with me, it still makes me happy to do this by myself.

_____

_____

_____

_____

_____

_____

_____

_____

What Makes Me Serene

Serene is a combination of happy and relaxed. It's the feeling that everything is right in my world. This is what gets me there.

Example: Being organized.

_____

_____

_____

_____

_____

_____

_____

_____

_____

_____

What I Do for You that Makes Me Happy

These are the things that make me happy to provide for you.

Example: Cooking yummy meals (but not every night).

_____

_____

_____

_____

_____

_____

_____

_____

_____

_____

_____

What Makes Me Tick

Now let's take a look at who you are and how you tick. This section really digs into how you work. You'll take a look at what you need, what you provide and a whole myriad of your own fantastic preferences.

Many of us are so busy figuring out what other people's needs and preferences are that we forget to consider our own. This section may be challenging, but it's definitely worth the effort! Check out the *Resources* section if you need some help.

Remember, you're allowed to think selfishly. It's just an exercise.

Do you know how dreams come true? First you have to dream them so you know what they are! That's your job now: to dream. (After that you can ask your loved ones for help with what you need. You may be pleasantly surprised to find that they are happy to provide for you!)

What I Provide

Here are three to five top qualities or behaviors I naturally bring to my relationships. These are the things I enjoy providing for you, the things my best self brings.

Example: Gentleness and playfulness.

What I Need

Do you know what you need?

For me, "need" was a foreign concept. If someone asked me what I needed or even offered me a glass of water, I'd say, "Oh, I'm fine. I don't need anything." One boyfriend said I was martyring myself – I had no idea what he was talking about (at the time).

Finally, I realized I was waking up tired, depressed and cranky, but I was still clueless. As luck would have it, I found my way to a workshop where I discovered how to focus on what I needed to be my best and what being my best self looks like. I gotta say, the exercise was a bit uncomfortable as the old record, in three-part harmony blared in my brain:

"No, no … I'm fine. Really, I'm fine … I don't need anything. Really. Fine here."

Figuring out what I needed was mind blowing yet incredibly simple. For example, here are a few of my needs:

- eight 8-ounce glasses of fresh water each day
- eight hours of sleep each night
- about one hour of wake-up-gently time

Was I getting these things? No! So, no wonder I was cranky!

Remember when I talked about the happiness deficit in the *Step 1: Decide What Makes You Happy* section? This *What I Need* section is about your basic human needs that get you just to neutral. Once these needs are met, you can start heaping on the happiness layer cake!

Do you know what you need to be your best self? I've got the next worksheet started for you, but feel free to add in more things.

What I Need

These are my basic human needs. These are the things that I need in order to be able to be my best self for me and you.

My Needs	Amount I Need	Notes & Tips
Food		
Water		
Sleep		
Sex		
Exercise		

My Needs	Amount I Need	Notes & Tips

Respect

A couple of years ago, a man I really liked said, "Tell me how you want to be respected, and I'll do it."

I gotta tell you, that blew my mind. What a great question. Now what's the answer? How *do* I want to be respected? What behaviors communicate respect for me? I know from working in the cultural melting pot of high tech that the definition of what behaviors are respectful varies by culture. When I lead a training class for Vettanna, I often bring up this topic for discussion, and the conversation always becomes quite spirited. It's a question most of us haven't considered except to know the feeling when we've been 'dissed (disrespected).

> "One thing I know for sure about men is that they really like to feel appreciated and acknowledged."
> – Joyce Arnowitz, Consultant

You may need to start with the behaviors that make you feel disrespected, and then work towards the positive behaviors that make you feel respected.

If you need help getting started, here are several examples of behaviors people find respectful. They are intentionally opposites; some will find the behavior in the first line respectful and others will find the behavior in the second line respectful.

***

Sally: I feel respected when I'm not interrupted while I'm speaking.

Josie: I feel respected when you finish my sentences; I feel like you really know me.

***

Pam: I feel respected when you say "thank you" for the meal I prepared, regardless of how tasty it is.

Val: I feel respected when you are totally honest about the quality of the meal I prepared. If you don't like it, tell me. Otherwise I'll make it again and keep making you suffer through it. Then no one is happy.

***

Tom: I feel respected when we have eye contact while I am speaking to you.

Tina: I feel respected when we don't have eye contact when I speak to you. I want to be able to speak my truth without responding to my perception of your reactions.

***

Betsy: I feel respected when people smile when I greet them.

Chen: I feel smiling is disrespectful and insincere.

***

Susie: I feel respected when my husband holds my hand in public. I feel like he is proud to be with me.

Marta: I feel any form of touching in public by a couple is disrespectful and should be private.

Can you see how important it is to define and discuss respect? If you don't, you leave a potential land mine that can explode in your relationship, usually when you least expect it.

What Makes Me Feel Respected

These are the behaviors that make me feel respected.

Example: Letting me finish my thought by not interrupting me while I'm talking, especially when I'm telling a story.

Frivolous Facts – Just For Fun!

Favorite flower:

Favorite florist (including address, phone or web site):

Favorite color:

Favorite food:

Favorite wine (please note, "red" and "white" are not enough information):

Favorite drink:

Favorite fruit:

Favorite restaurant in the world (including address, phone or website):

Favorite local restaurant (including address, phone or website):

Favorite TV show:

Favorite movie:

Favorite band:

Favorite sport to watch:

Favorite sports team:

Favorite sport to play:

Favorite travel destination:

What I'd like to learn:

What I ache for:

What I fear most:

Level of competitive drive in sports, work and life:

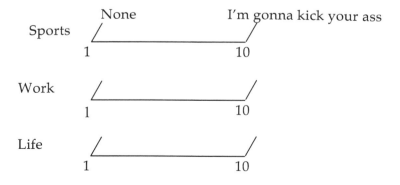

Dates I'd Like to Go On

These are the dates I'd like to go on. I've included addresses and phone numbers if reservations are required.

Example:

$0	Short hikes, bonus if you bring a picnic
$	Movies (i.e. comedy, drama, chick flicks)
$$$$$	London vacation

Cost Key:

$0	Free
$	Cheap, under $50
$$	Around $100
$$$	Between $100 - $1,000
$$$$$	Save up for this cuz I am so worth it!

Cost	Event	Location, Contact, Web

Cost	Event	Location, Contact, Web

Presents I Like

These are the presents I like to receive. I've included estimated cost, websites, addresses or phone numbers so you can easily find them.

Example: $10   iTunes gift certificate   www.apple.com/itunes

Cost	Item	Location, Contact, Web

Cost	Item	Location, Contact, Web

Favorite "Cheats"

These are the yummy treats I really shouldn't have, but on very limited occasions they make me really happy. I've included the address or website so you can easily find them.

Example: Teuscher Chocolates, champagne truffles (only two, please) 307 Sutter Street in Union Square, San Francisco. www.teuschersf.com

"Cheat"	Where

"Cheat"	Where

I Really Don't Like

These are the things I really have an aversion to.
Example: I hate being cold.

_____

_____

_____

_____

_____

_____

_____

_____

_____

_____

_____

_____

When I'm Sick

These things would help me out when I'm sick. Please remember I probably won't have the energy or presence of mind to make the happy face that shows my appreciation until I feel better.

Example: Make sure I have tissues and water. Please cook.

_____

_____

_____

_____

_____

_____

_____

_____

_____

_____

Freaking Out

In a perfect world, there would be no freak outs. But we're not living in that world yet! That means there are basically two kinds of freak outs – the kind where the world has gone crazy...and the kind where our sweetie, um... blundered!

When I'm Emotional and It's Not About You

These things happen. I get upset from time to time. When it's not about you, here's how you can support me and help me feel normal again.

*Example: Listen, but ask if I want help solving it **before** you offer suggestions.*

_____

_____

_____

_____

_____

_____

When I'm Emotional and You're Involved

When I'm upset with you, here's how you can support me and help me feel normal again.

Example: Please say you're sorry for hurting my feelings.

_____

_____

_____

_____

_____

_____

_____

_____

_____

Who You (My Happiness Bringer) Are

Now it's time to explore your happiness bringer, the person(s) who will ultimately read your *Happiness Handbook*, and the qualities and behaviors they have that meet your minimum requirements. In most cases your reader will be your current significant other. If you don't have one (or are contemplating upgrading) then the reader will be the person you are envisioning or courting to become your significant other. It's possible that you could be writing this with your parent, child, roommate or even someone else in mind; with that being said, I'll use the term "reader" from here out. You can pick another term that is more meaningful for you, if you like (i.e.: sweetie, main squeeze, BFF).

If you already have a sweetie or reader in your life, it's still valuable and interesting to take the time to define the list of qualities and behaviors that you need in them. Do this list as if the reader was not in your life right now. When you are done, read it and see how close the reader comes to meeting your needs.

> *"One thing I know for sure about men is they like to solve the problem."*
> – Grace Kang, Owner, Pink Olive Boutique

You can have your reader take a look at the list and see how close they come. Maybe they are only off on one or two items. That might lead to an interesting dialog and maybe even result in a few modifications that wind up with you getting your needs met. How cool would that be?!

Chocolate Receiver and Olive Bringer

 When you're done with your lists, you may realize that you are a "chocolate receiver." You *neeeeed* chocolate and your list defines a wonderful chocolate bringer BUT you are in a relationship with a natural olive bringer. The olive bringer is a lovely person but not someone who is a natural chocolate bringer. In fact, it wouldn't even occur to the olive bringer to stroll down the chocolate aisle at the store, much less seek out artisan chocolate sources. They probably can't figure out why the expensive olives they bring aren't evoking your happy dance.

Now what? Can you train a natural olive bringer to become a chocolate bringer or can you switch to being a happy olive receiver? Or do you kick 'em to the curb and begin the quest for the chocolate bringer of your dreams? Well, that's up to you. But at least you know you have a mismatch in your happiness needs and in the natural qualities of your bringer. (You realize that this isn't just about olives and chocolate, right?)

Who You (My Happiness Bringer) Are

These are the qualities I need in you and love you for.
Example: You are honest. You laugh at my jokes and stories.

Top Five Deal Breakers

These are the five things I absolutely must have in a relationship.

Example: Monogamy. No substance abuse. Humor

_____

_____

_____

_____

_____

_____

_____

_____

_____

Sex

Feel free to take your time on this section. Have a glass of wine, light some candles, relax, explore, and get into a rhythm. *Or* you could speed it up and breeze through it. *Or* you could mix up the pace – a little fast, a little slow ... Oh, I'm distracted. I'm talking about your writing – yes, really I am.

Think of this section as your treasure map to bliss. You want to give your reader (your "pirate," if that works for you!) good directions so they don't veer too far off the map and miss the treasure entirely.

And in all seriousness, only do the sections you feel comfortable with. If you're not comfortable with this section at all, skip it or rip it out. It's your user's manual. The only person you have to please is yourself. No one will grade it, critique it, verify you completed it, and you won't offend me by ripping it up or skipping it. It's your happiness ... whatever gets you there!

Answers to the Top Eight Questions

1. How much sex do I need?

2. What percentage do I need to be the rip-our-clothes-off, let's-get-to-it version and what percentage needs to be the softer, sweeter, more connected love making?

3. What's my favorite time of day for sex?

4. What's my favorite position?

5. What do I want to explore?

6. When don't I want sex?

7. Is there a time I might want sex, but you wouldn't think so?

8. Do I like being the ravisher or being ravished? (Ravish not radish!)

The Spots That "Do" Me

When you touch or kiss these spots ... oh yeah, baby! In the immortal words of James Brown, *"I Feel Good!"*

Example: Kissing –"Long, slow, wet kisses that last for three days" (paraphrased from the movie Bull Durham).

_____

_____

_____

_____

_____

_____

_____

_____

_____

Signs I'm "In the Mood"

Here's how you'll know I'm feeling a little frisky.
Example: My toes curl.

What I'd Like to Do to You

In my wildest dreams, these are some of the things I'd like to do to you.

Example: I'd like to rip your shirt open.

_____

_____

_____

_____

_____

_____

_____

_____

_____

_____

The Perfect Moment Below the Belt

If you were to give me the perfect experience when your kisses explore the far end of my universe, this is what you'd do.

Example: You'd start by softly kissing the inside of my thigh ...

_____

_____

_____

_____

_____

_____

_____

_____

_____

_____

The Perfect "After"

Here's what makes me happy after "the deed" is done.

Example: You hold me in your arms and tell me how much I rock your world.

_____

_____

_____

_____

_____

_____

_____

_____

_____

_____

More Information, Stories and Fantasies

Your reader may need some more information or stories or fantasies. Here's where you can add a little more information. Remember to include what you need before, during and after sex too.

_____

_____

_____

_____

_____

_____

_____

_____

_____

_____

The Dark Side

Everyone's got one. So let's get it out in the open.

Some of your dark side items may be things that you are consciously working to improve. Others may be things that you accept about yourself; you are not working on them and you hope your happiness bringer can accept them, too.

What's a dark side? It's the quintessential "bad behaviors" or the stuff that just makes you cranky. They could be as easy as:

I bite my nails on Tuesdays. I'm trying to change … maybe I'll try Fridays instead.

Or they could be a little more complex, for example:

I drink too much on my birthday. I hate the next morning, but I always have so much fun that night. I like my little birthday vice, and I've got no intention of toning it down.

Ahh, just so you know, I made up both of those examples. Not that they are bad. I'm just saying…I've got different vices!

Wouldn't it be cool if you "confessed" your dark side to your happiness bringer and they responded with, "Oh that's not so bad" or "I can live with that." I gotta say, that response would make me happy!

Now, turn down the lights, and let's take a walk on your dark side. The next four pages cover your dark side in different ways and degrees.

What Bugs Me

These are the behaviors or things that bug me. They are things that can send me into an upset place. (If that happens, see the *Freaking Out* section.)

Example: People who don't keep their commitments to me. Renegotiation is acceptable and encouraged. Reset my expectations, but please don't break them.

_____

_____

_____

_____

_____

_____

_____

_____

_____

Big Deals

These are the things that are big deals to me in life. I've included a story or explanation why to give you some insight.

Example: I work a lot, most of it behind the scenes. I need to be "seen" and thanked for my efforts. "Thank you" is like money in the bank for me. It really feeds me and keeps me motivated.

_____

_____

_____

_____

_____

_____

_____

_____

_____

Receiving Feedback

If you need to give me feedback, suggestions or criticism, here's how I best receive it.

Example: I respond best if feedback is given lightly and without a critical tone of voice. Please provide examples of when I did the "thing," and examples of how you'd like me to do or be instead. Please tell me how it made you feel or affected you so I can have compassion for you and understand how my behavior affected you. The compassion will help motivate me to change.

The Dark Side –
Bad Habits That Just Are

These are the facets of my personality that are not all sweetness and light. They are my inner demons I have come to accept. (I hope you will, too.) I've indicated whether they are something I'm working on or ... not.

Example: I have a hard time doing or finishing mundane things. I'm not working to change this other than by delegating them. (i.e.: you can balance the checkbook.)

_____

_____

_____

_____

_____

_____

_____

_____

Living an Extraordinary Life

A couple years ago, a friend of mine, who was a sophomore in college at the time, sent me an email asking, "What's the definition of an extraordinary life?" This question lead to a several month-long email discourse about the qualities of an extraordinary life. Who is the definer of an extraordinary life? Is it a social norm, a pop culture definition, a familial response or an individual choice?

We came to the conclusion that it is an individual choice that may be flavored by other influences. We observed that for some people, an extraordinary life is defined by living in a small town and raising a happy family; for others, it is a life of service; and yet for others, it is marked by achievement.

> "What makes me happy is peace and quiet."
> – Michelle Dench,
> CEO of Sustainable Financial

Some months later, I mentioned to him that I had the opportunity to go to London for a few weeks, but was considering not going. Based upon what was happening in my industry and my company, it seemed a bit irresponsible to take a couple weeks off and blow a chunk of change on travel, fine food and fantastic shows. He shot an email right back, challenging my decision based upon what I had shared as my definition of living an extraordinary life. He reminded me that it included travel, fine food and the arts, and that London is one of my favorite cities.

I must say it was a bit humbling to be mentored by someone I was supposed to be mentoring! But he was absolutely right. I booked the ticket and made a conscious choice to move forward in my life, making decisions based upon my definition of an extraordinary life. I'm glad I went; it was a life-defining moment and a blissfully life-changing trip for me.

After all is said and done, won't it be satisfying to look back upon your life and know that it was well lived, whatever your definition?

My Extraordinary Life

When I listen to my heart, this is my definition of an extraordinary life.

Example: Taking a couple trips each year. Staying in posh hotels, eating fine food, experiencing the arts and culture of the places I visit.

_____

_____

_____

_____

_____

_____

_____

_____

_____

_____

_____

Life Purpose

So what is your life purpose? It's really not as hard to figure out as you may think.

It's to live your extraordinary life.

It sounds so simple.

Will it be easy? Probably not.

Will it be worth it? Most certainly.

It will be an adventure that will fill you up and satisfy you like nothing else.

Now, go do it.

Live your passion.

Be happy.

Have your life just the way you want it for yourself.

Live your extraordinary life!

I wish you much happiness,

Jenn

Troubleshooting

Defining Happiness

When you're having difficulty figuring out what makes you happy, here are some ideas to help you ignite your creativity.

Five Imaginary Lives

This is an exercise from *The Artist's Way* by Julia Cameron. Tarcher, 2002. You can either daydream and imagine or write down five different lives you might like to live in your wildest dreams. This isn't practical stuff; this is the fun stuff. You can just wave a magic wand and "poof, you're a doctor" – you skipped through the whole med school/residency thing and now you're the top dude in your field, making beau coup bucks, helping people feel better, and golfing on the weekends.

Let your imagination run wild. Anything from rock star to president to truck driver to parent is fair game. No one will read it, criticize or critique your dream. This is just for you. From your wildest dreams, you should be able to find some tidbits that you can add to your happy-making list. For example, in the imaginary doctor's life example, maybe it's helping people that makes you happy, or maybe it's golf!

A year after I did this exercise, I realized I wasn't living one of those lives, I had incorporated parts of each of my five imaginary lives into the life I'm now living. I think that's so cool!

Date Yourself

Yes, put a date on the calendar and take yourself out. Become your own happiness bringer. If you had a two- to three-hour hour date with yourself, what would you do? You can't do chores or tasks or get organized or catch up. If you'd just met a hot, new sweetie, you wouldn't do that on one of your dates (I hope). So, what would you do?

> "One thing I know for sure about men is they are in awe of the feminine."
> – Aimee Lyndon-Adams,
> Founder, What Truly Matters

You are dating a hot, new sweetie – you! What would make you happy? Mini golf? An art museum, play or concert? Playing or watching a sporting event? Sky diving? Taking a class and learning something new? Shopping? Going to the spa or a monster truck rally? It's your time, and it's all about what makes you happy. You work hard; you deserve a couple of hours of happiness. Now, go and make it so, and remember to add it to your happiness list!

Here's one way it works for me: every 12 weeks, I get my hair cut in Union Square in San Francisco, and this becomes a perfect day I provide myself. I get my makeup done at Saks, shop (or window shop) at some amazing stores and boutiques, and end my day by getting one champagne truffle from my favorite chocolatier. I drive home in bliss.

Vision Board/Collage

Consider checking out the book *Creative Visualization* by Shakti Gawain. New World Press, 2002. Create a collage/vision board of happy-making things and people. Vision boards were also referenced in the movie *The Secret* produced by Rhonda Byrne. Prime Time Productions, 2006. They help keep you focused and draw into your life things, people and feelings.

Guided Meditations

Try one or more of the guided mediations created specifically to help you through this book in *The Happiness Handbook Meditation CD*. If you've never meditated before, relax. This CD and the exercises in this book are more like playing "theatre of the mind" than sitting on a cushion for an extended time. I start you out easy by helping you create a safe, fun place in your mind to go to when you work through what makes you happy or releasing fear or anger. Available at www.happiness-handbook.com

Fear

Some of us have had traumatic moments in the past that cause us to be fearful now. Fear of people, places or things, or fear of letting people get close to us. Take a deep breath. We're going to dive in and see if we can loosen up some of this fear with baby steps. Your fear is absolutely valid and probably "saved" you in the past. But you're older now and more capable of handling situations. Be gentle as you move this one. It's huge, I know.

One of the things about fear is that it's often based upon something that happened in the past. Here's an exercise to try. If it doesn't work, if your fear leans more towards terror or if your fear is from physical harm, consider working with a professional who can support you and help you move through it.

A New Outcome

Find a quiet spot where you won't be disturbed and feel totally safe. You can do this as a meditation, a daydream or you can write it out.

Imagine that a bubble of bright white light surrounds and protects you. Imagine a rose is floating in front of you outside of the bubble. Now, think about the fear and feel where it is in your body. Let's start with your head. Imagine the fear as a physical object or a color. In your mind's eye, take the fear and move it into the rose. If you've seen the Harry Potter movie, it can be like the scene where Dumbledore moves the threads of memory into the pensieve.

If the fear is anywhere else in your body, like your heart, throat, stomach, arms or legs, do the same fear-moving process.

The next step is to brainstorm different choices you could make or behaviors you could chose if that situation or a similar one ever arose again. Some options are fight (physically or verbally), flight, freeze or defuse.

Imagine yourself safe, confident, secure, powerful and strong. Now picture the fear event happening again, but this time imagine you made a different choice. How does the scenario plays out? This is called performance visualization, and it's a technique athletes use before a competition. When you can visualize a positive outcome and retain your feeling of strength, confidence and safety, run the scenario through your mind several more times, each time focusing on the feeling in your body.

Fear's a tricky thing. If this helps, great. If not, keep seeking alternatives to help you move through or clear the fear altogether. Take heart, nearly everyone has fear. You are ahead of the game when you know what yours is and you actively work to shift it.

Fear of Revealing Yourself

What if your fear stems from people picking on you or having had your diaries stolen and your private thoughts being read and even made fun of?

The thought of writing down anything about ourselves can bring up some fear. First, let me say how sorry I am that you had that experience. Here are three suggestions for working with the fear of revealing yourself:

1. An Exercise

Instead of writing down your thoughts, consider this book merely an exercise in clarifying your thoughts so that you can verbalize them to your loved ones in a clear, concise manner. Just think about each section, don't write anything. You can do that another time, if and when you feel more comfortable.

"One thing I know for sure about men is they need love just as much as we do."
– Michelle Dench, CEO, Sustainable Financial

2. Lock It Up

Writing out your thoughts and seeing them on paper has many benefits. It stimulates more thoughts and clarity, and it honors your needs and desires when they are in a form that you (or others) can see.

Try writing out your thoughts and locking them up. I actually have a hidden box of old journals that I've entrusted a friend to toss out, immediately upon my death. When you are in the process of working things out, your thoughts and writings are in the moment and not meant to be read by others. Feel free to consider this part of your process. You can choose if and when you are comfortable to share your writing with another person.

3. Get Over It

This is the hard-line approach. Don't feel pressured to take it; it's just another option. Perhaps fear served you well in the past, but consider the option of letting it go, moving on and making a different choice. This new choice is designed to help you be happy. Consider that a good thing. Check out the tools in the *Troubleshooting* section to help you release the fear.

If you have fear around this in any way, no matter what option you choose, know that you are brave and you are moving forward. Good for you!

Getting Unstuck or Getting To Neutral

If you've gotten stuck on any of the sections, relax. It's totally normal. No one expected you to just whip right through this workbook. Some thoughts take time to "cook" and develop, and some need "space" in order to make themselves clear. Being stuck is a normal part of the journey (dang it), and you're bound to release some old crap and/or uncover some juicy bits as you "unstick" yourself.

Making Space

Imagine that your brain is like your closet. You may need to do a little spring-cleaning and get rid of the old thoughts and emotions that don't suit you anymore. Maybe it's time to let go of old anger or resentment.

Consider this: Yes, you got hurt. Yes, the person who hurt you is a real piece of work. But they are probably gone from your life by now. They can't hurt you anymore. You no longer need to protect yourself. They can't feel your wrath. Your continuing to be angry doesn't affect them – but it does affect you. Maybe it's time to make a new choice.

Fire Them or Set Them Free

This next one you can use while you are meditating or doing "The Chair" exercise that's explained in the next few pages. Bring to mind the person who hurt you (or an aspect of yourself that you no longer want around); now fire them from whatever role they played in your life. Their performance was clearly not up to your standards. What if the person is your parent, can you fire them? Sure, it's your imagination; feel free to use it creatively. You may not want to do it in person though, since it could have bridge-burning consequences and our ultimate goal is to just give you peace of mind. If firing is a little harsh, how about demoting them to a "junior" position where they have less power, authority and influence.

"One thing I know for sure about men is to just keep it simple!"
– Deb Fallon, Project Manager

If the firing metaphor doesn't work, try setting them free. Imagine driving the person who hurt you someplace (like the desert, coffee shop or the mall) have a "goodbye" conversation that makes you feel good, and then let them out of the car. Now imagine driving off. Feel the emotions; hopefully they include relief, peace or joy. Know there's never any wrong emotion; whatever comes up for you is good. (Remember, this is in your imagination. I'm not advocating leaving grandma in Death Valley for real!)

Cut the Link

In the section on *How to Figure Out What Makes You Happy*, there's a subsection called *Reminisce and Fantasize*, I ask you to recall a past event that made you happy but not to think about how the relationship eventually soured and ended. OK, granted this is a big getting stuck spot. Your brain is hardwired to connect that happy event with the eventual descent into hell. Fair enough.

"One thing I know for sure about men is they are not mind readers; ask (sweetly) for what you want ladies!" – Ayesha Mathews-Wadhwa, CEO of PixInk Design

But … the happy-making event did not lead to the demise of the relationship, and if you have a similar happy-making event now, it will not foretell the end of this relationship. (OK, probably not. I could be wrong, but work with me on this one.)

Maybe you need to recall the whole relationship in all its magnificent glory and all its mucky defeat. As you do, write down all of the happiness things. Now, get in your quiet space and imagine yourself in whatever place makes you feel good. Maybe it's outside; maybe you'll need a long table in this exercise with you at one end and the table between you and the other stuff we're about to bring in. You may want to imagine some strong helpers with you, supportive people in your life or a guardian angel or God. When this exercise is over, you can use your mind's eye to give these helpful people a high five!

Once you're in your perfect spot with your helpful person or people behind you, do one or both of the following things:

1. Imagine the happiness event, and then imagine the bitter end or the eventual negative result. Imagine a cord connecting the two. This symbolizes the neural pathway in your brain that sees the happiness then sees the pain. Now,

imagine you have scissors or a knife or a big old honking sword (whatever it takes) and, in your imagination, cut the link between that happiness event and the pain. Imagine your support team cheering you, proud of you, giving high fives and hugs.

You can repeat this for other happiness events, too. How do you know which ones to do? When you think of a happiness event, does it make you sad instead of happy? Those are the ones to do. For example, maybe you love bowling but this sweetie you were so in love with broke up with you while you were happy and bowling. Now the thought of going bowling makes you wistful and a bit sad, and not all fired up and ready to rent shoes!

> "What makes me happy is to be near or in the water, completely relaxing and enjoying, the tranquility and beauty."
> – Joyce Arnowitz, Consultant

As you end your imaginary event, remember to turn and thank your helpful people team.

2. Imagine across from you is the former happiness bringer who also brought you pain. Imagine a cord connecting you two. Take a moment to tell the person what good stuff they brought to your life. In your imagination, tell them about the stuff they did to hurt you. Can you thank them for the life lesson and tell them it's time to move on? If you're not to that spot yet, that's OK. Now, in your imagination, get out your scissors, knife or sword, and cut the cord. Send them on their way, and thank your support team.

Pretend

Remember when you were a kid and you pretended you were a cowboy, astronaut, firefighter, doctor or mom? You found "props" and acted out scenes and were happy ... and playful.

What if now – hang with me here – you did the same thing? Get some props and, in the privacy of your home, act it out. This can take mental "crap" and physically move it through and *out* of your body. I'm a little embarrassed to tell you this story, but here's how this worked for me. A while back I felt like I was blocked. I couldn't move forward in life, business, relationship and music. It was really frustrating. I did a meditation and got the feeling and the visual that I was bound or tied (hence the not being able to move). So, I went to the toy store and bought a plastic Excalibur sword. Then when I was alone, I laid on the floor with the sword at my side. I did a little meditation and got myself to the feeling of being bound and unable to move, and I summoned my courage (and anger), grabbed the sword and cut through the imaginary bonds … slaying the (mental) dragon that was bugging me. It worked. I felt much better, and things started moving in my life. Allowing myself to be goofy and playful helped me tap back into some of the pure joy I had when I was little. Now, I try to keep that playfulness alive. And, yes, I've still got the sword … but shhhh, my nephew thinks I got it for him ;-).

Moving

Sometimes when you're stuck in your mind, moving real things helps. For example:

- Move your furniture around
- Clean a closet
- Spring-clean your home or car
- File the piles of paper that are sitting around
- Throw/give away the piles of magazines or books you've been meaning to clear out

Sometimes, manual labor can help unlock stuckness. So, get out and garden, build something, sweep something, or walk your neighborhood with a trash bag and gloves, picking up little bits of trash that are laying around.

Finally, if you're stuck in despair and depression, getting off the couch might seem like an insurmountable task. So, here's your assignment and it's totally do-able!

1. **3 at 3**: Every day at 3:00 take three deep breaths. Really fill your lungs, feeling them expand and contract as air enters and leaves. Pay attention to your eyes and your brain, as you practice this, you'll start to feel a lightening or lifting or tingling sensation as the air starts "waking up" your cells. (It doesn't need to be 3:00 by the way). Set a timer, so you remember to do it every day.

2. **3 at 3, 6, and 9**: Next do it more than once a day. You could try 3:00, 6:00 and 9:00. You could do it before you get out of bed in the morning and at mealtime. If you're grazing, do it every time you grab a snack!

3. **Butts UP for 3**: Now that you're taking in all that air, it's time to find some that's fresh. Let's not call this a walk just yet. We're taking baby steps. Go outside and take three deep breaths of fresh air. Walk to the end of your driveway (or a little way) take three more deep breaths. Walk back to your door and take three more deep breaths before you going into your house. Gradually increase your distance until you walk down the block and back.

4. **Walk**: Now you're ready for a full-on walk, whether it's around the block, down to the coffee shop or on a nature trail. Remember to take a couple of your deep breaths as you walk. If you walk to the coffee shop, the snack in the middle of your walk will be a reward, plus it will get you interacting with some other folks (who may actually be doing the same thing!)

Before you know it, you'll have moved some of the fog and begun your journey toward happiness. And soon you'll be ready to experiment with some of the other techniques here that can help you move your emotions, get to neutral and then to happiness.

One thing you must promise me though: Never, ever, ever feel bad for finding yourself at the despair, sorrow, depressed stuck spot (even if you've been there a long time). Crap happened, and emotions set in. That's how we are setup as humans; it's our automatic response. It's your choice to begin the journey of transforming your "crap" into "parc" … you were supposed to laugh here at the really bad use of spelling crap backwards to illustrate your transformation. (Remember, I warned you that I'm kind of goofy!)

Oh, and if you happen to be on any meds or under a doctor's care please always heed their advice first. The stuff I'm talking about here should be "play" and not a replacement for the help you are already getting.

Clear the Anger

A couple other things can help you "clear anger," moving it from your mind, through your body and out. It's a good idea to make the agreement with yourself that this is it; this is the last time you're going to be this charged up and angry about this thing or person. So, you can really let 'er rip.

The Chair

When you are home alone, sit in a chair with another chair facing you. Visualize (imagine) the person with whom you are angry or upset sitting in the other chair. You've got this person's full, undivided attention (in your imagination), and they are not going to interrupt or talk back! So, let it all out. Tell them why you're mad. Rehash the mad-making event. Yell and scream (you may want a little pillow nearby to scream into so the neighbors don't freak out!) After you feel spent, your part is done.

You can end the exercise, or you can imagine that the person is suddenly a paragon of virtue and maturity. You can imagine them acknowledging that they hurt you and apologizing. In your perfect world (and it is, cuz it's your imagination) what would you need them to say in order for you to feel complete or better?

If you're feeling mature (which is not a requirement for this exercise), you can even imagine thanking them for the life lesson, shaking their hand and sending them on their way. Again, not required. The big point of this exercise is just getting the anger out of your brain and your body.

This one really works for me, and I use it a lot. I actually use it when I'm angry with someone *before* I talk to him or her about it. This way, I get all of the anger out (as well as the "and another thing!" that women tend to do in fights!) It also works as a dress rehearsal, and helps me find the point and the right way to say it so I can use a normal tone of voice instead of the angry tone that's not so appealing (or effective)!

At Bat

 I love this one! If you've got a batting cage in town, find it. Wear comfortable clothes and gym shoes (no hard-soled shoes or heels). For less than $10 you can rent a bat, a helmet and a whole slew of balls. Whether you've ever played baseball or softball, doesn't matter. (If you haven't played, pick the softballs, they are larger than baseballs and easier to hit). As you stand in the batting cage, imagine the thing or person you are angry at and as the ball comes toward you, WHACK! If there's not a lot of people or any children around, you can even add sound effects like "you f*&%er" as you connect bat and ball.

One time I was about to bat, and a dad and his 10-year old boy sat down to wait for their turn. Dang, no sound effects for me! But I got my anger out and nailed all 25 balls, bam, bam, bam. I got my little release, and as I opened the cage and walked out, the dad said, "Wow! That was incredible!" I replied, "You have no idea."

Recently, I had the need again. As I went to pay, the high school kid at the counter said, "Gotta get your ya-yas out, huh?" I said, a bit embarrassed, "Is it that obvious?" Luckily the kid replied, "No, it's just that when people arrive dressed in their work clothes, we figure they've got something to work through other than trying to increase their batting average."

Plates

 I have a friend who has an interesting spin on the bat idea. She goes to garage sales and buys cheap, ceramic plates and flat bed sheets. When she's "ready," she tapes a couple sheets to the wall of the garage and lays some on the floor, making sure they overlap. Then she stands back, with goggles on, and wails the plates at the wall. When she's done, she scoops up the sheets with the broken pieces of china on them and pops them in the trash. Personally, I prefer to vent in ways that don't require cleanup, but she swears by this one ... or is it *during* this one! ;-)

Sorrow or Anger in Five Minutes a Day

This book was on the way to the publisher a while back when I hit a triple whammy of sorrow-making events. I got knocked down so hard, I put the book on pause because, in all integrity, I couldn't release a book on happiness when I felt decimated. These were big "loosing people" events, not "oh shoot, Peet's is out of lattes today" events.

If I knew what would make me happy, why didn't I just do it and snap out of it already? Believe me, I gave that a try. But I think with big sorrow, it's the "feeling it" that heals it, and feeling it takes time.

After escaping into work and TV, the one thing that helped was making a deal with myself that I would find a quiet five minutes every day with a box of Kleenex and just let the sorrow be. Allow myself to feel it in all its intensity. OK, it lasted more than five minutes at first, but eventually I sat down for my quiet time and was just done. I'd come back to my neutral. That's when I remembered that sorrow puts you into a massive happiness deficit, and you've got to gently work your way back to neutral before your happy-making actions will actually produce happy dances.

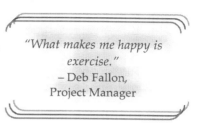

"What makes me happy is exercise."
– Deb Fallon,
Project Manager

Are you here? If you are, whether you see it now or not, there is light (and happiness) at the end of the tunnel. You've got to go through that dark tunnel to get there. You can do it! Eventually you'll only need four minutes a day, and one day you'll sit down and realize you aren't angry or sad about this thing any more. You've worked it out!

If you are overwhelmed with sorrow or anger, try doing the opposite; allow yourself to practice being happy for just five minutes each day. Remember what it feels like in your mind and body. Eventually build up to more than five minutes a day.

Accountability

You'll notice this one is near the end, not only because it's the one we avoid, but also because it's often easier to get the anger out *at* the other person than it is to look at ourselves and take responsibility.

This exercise requires you to write down *every* time in your life you have purposefully done something wrong. Don't justify it; simply name it. It's also good to include as much as you can remember about the event. For example:

It was a sunny August day. I was five. My brother and I were playing in the sandbox and I punched him in the face.

Justifying it would be to add:

He called me a "poop head," so I punched him.

Don't justify. Just write the action that you did. (Also please note that my brothers were not yet born when I was five; I made that one up.)

Also write down every time that you withheld something from someone. It could be ignoring someone, zoning out while they were talking or choosing not to provide comfort when they needed it. For example:

Last week, I didn't call that guy back.

OK, I didn't make this one up. In my defense, I'm much better with email. Oops, that's a justification. Dang it!

When you're done, you'll have a stack of paper and hopefully the feeling of "ahh" and sense of completion. Then you can do a couple of different things.

1. Some people say you need to have someone else read them; the act of another person knowing is how the release happens. (The other person is a witness and makes sure you didn't justify.)

2. Others suggest burning the papers in a fireplace. I prefer this method, but I have done it both ways.

The thing I find interesting about this exercise is how hard it is to take such a scathing look at my behaviors over my life and how I suddenly am able to connect the dots. For example, I saw that my withholding attention and affection caused the same kinds of behaviors in the other people. That was a real eye opener; an actual cause or trigger to the other people's bad behavior toward me. Ooohhh.

Now I know I need to be mindful and responsible enough to make a different choice when I get into a situation where my instinctive response is to withhold. Drat, we're back to maturity again!

Play

We've now done all sorts of work to get ourselves unstuck. It's time to go play. Have fun. Move your body. Don't work out or do a task; *play*. Like when you were a kid. Swing on a swing, run, skip, jump, and dance, play in a sand box or the water, or take a bubble bath with tub toys! Whatever makes you feel movement in your body and causes you to breathe deep into your lungs, do it. Maybe the physical activity will help "unstick" you. Speaking of physical activities ... *there's* an idea for playful, adult fun ;-)

> "*One thing I know for sure about men is that they will do anything they can to support you and your dreams if they love you unconditionally ... even when you act like a total psycho b**ch at times!*"
> – Lori Fuller, Photographer

Diet

One last comment on getting unstuck; consider your diet. My own personal experiments have led me to the conclusion that sugar and alcohol make me feel less happy – or even not happy at all – for a few days after I've consumed them. (Dang it!) Yes, I still cheat and eat yummy things that are bad for me from time to time. But when I'm walking along and realize I'm bitchin' and moaning when just the other day I was perky and happy, I think back to what I ate and, more often than not, I've had chocolate or ice cream or chips or French fries ... or a margarita (did I mention dang it?!) Anyway, diet may be another place for you to experiment. Yes, I know how hard it is to get off sugar. You'll need determination and perseverance, but you can do it. For me it's kind of like crack; if I go back on it, it's hard to get off again. So, it makes the staying off a little easier. I've also got so much more energy and vitality when I'm eating healthy; that's a real bonus.

Tips for Getting Off of Sugar or Chocolate

The biggest problem with sugar and chocolate for me is I get a "taste" for it in my mouth; here are a few things that have worked for me:

1. Don't have any sweets or chocolate in the house. And don't drive to any store while you're having a craving.

2. Eat a pickle or some olives. This puts an entirely different flavor in your mouth that's not complementary to sugar.

3. Drink water. Sometimes what you really need is water, and your body's signals get switched. The body says "water" but the mouth hears "sweets." Try water first.

4. Drink a spicy tea. I like Celestial Seasoning's Bengal Spice or Market Spice Tea from Seattle's Pike Place Market. Both are available on Amazon, and they are good at putting a different flavor in my mouth, distracting me from sweets.

5. Think about what you are doing when the taste or craving pops up. I tend to get cravings on days I'm not very active or I'm working long jags at the computer. If I get up, drink water, maybe have an olive and then walk the dog, those things make me forget the craving. Going to workout is good, too.

6. Think about what you are thinking when the taste or craving sets in. If I'm pouting and feeling sorry for myself, singing "he done me wrong" songs, I tend to get all crave-y. The obvious answer here is to do the *Getting Unstuck* exercises, but the reality is ... I'm not always that evolved and sometimes I need a good mope.

This is the hardest time for me to avoid sweets, especially chocolate. A good cry, a long walk, a drive in the car singing all those emotive love-lost ballads, a glass of water ... these all help. I've even called a friend to "confess," that I was moping and craving, hoping the shame will snap me out of it.

I had the best luck a couple weeks ago. I was in the chocolate aisle at the market and a woman asked if her cart was blocking my view. I said, "No, I'm just contemplating if I should be bad or not." And with a stroke of sheer brilliance she said, "Oh, don't do it." Score! That was all I needed. I thanked her and walked to the checkout.

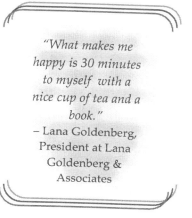

"What makes me happy is 30 minutes to myself with a nice cup of tea and a book."
– Lana Goldenberg, President at Lana Goldenberg & Associates

Receiving

Many of us are so used to giving to others that we haven't paid attention to how we receive when someone gives something to us. Here are a couple ideas to help you receive graciously.

A Glass of Water

When you arrive in someone's home, they will often politely offer you a glass of water or something to drink. If you usually say "no, thank you" because you don't want to bother them, view this as an opportunity to practice receiving. Try saying "yes, please," remembering to thank them and smile. (No happy dance though, that's probably a little over the top just for water. But you could, I won't stop your happiness experience!)

Reframing the Offer

I touched on something above that I'd like to delve into a bit more. It's the concept of making a decision for the giver as to whether it will be an imposition or too much trouble for them to give. Please stop that. The person offered you something. Consider that they already ran it through their own "is this too big of a deal" filter before making the offer.

> "One thing I know for sure about men is when they love us, they do so with whole mind, body and spirit. And, when they say they don't want to get married, they are not lying."
> – Julie Steelman, Sales Consultant and Author

Think about your frame of mind when you offer someone something. You're probably happy and ready to do the giving. You want the other person to receive. You want to make them happy. It makes you happy to make them happy.

Let me repeat that please.

It makes you happy to make them happy.

Let's follow this logic. When you offer something and the person accepts, they are happy to receive the thing and it makes you happy to be their happiness bringer. If they were to refuse, they would be withholding happiness from themselves *and* from you.

That means the opposite is true. When you decide for the giver that it's too much for them to do and you refuse, you are withholding happiness from yourself and from the potential giver.

Look, I get tripped up on this one all the time. Go back to the glass of water exercise, and start there. It'll be good practice for when someone offers to loan you his or her car or vacation home!

Dinner

Here's another easy way to practice. When you go out to dinner, practice being a gracious receiver with your waiter. Say "yes, please" when they offer you water or ketchup. Say "thank you" and smile when they bring your food, the bill or the tab. Watch their response. Do they smile, stand a little straighter or does their face soften? It doesn't work with all waiters, of course. But it's not about their response; it's about you getting some safe and easy practice being a receiver.

The Power of Your Mind

When I was so unhappy and just working toward getting to neutral, there were a couple of things I did with my mind. You may think they are kooky, dumb or silly. That's fine. I'm cool with that. I tried them, they helped me, and I'm happy now.

Positive Reinforcement

Ask your sweetie or support team (your friends or your guardian angels) to provide you with acknowledgement and positive reinforcement as they see you implementing the new behaviors of asking for what you need/want and actively receiving.

Rewiring

This exercise is based upon the information in the movie *What The Bleep* where quantum physicists determined thinking negative thoughts actually erodes the neural pathways of positive thoughts.

Before you go to sleep or get out of bed, visualize little pathways in your brain and repeat to yourself a little mantra: "I am consciously connecting the neural networks and neural paths for _____." Some examples might be love, happiness, gratitude, receiving, etc. Visualize the little pathways, like train tracks or roads, opening up, and let yourself experience the feeling of the emotion you are "turning back on."

Physical Pain

If you have physical pain and are working on this book, good for you for taking action. But go easy on yourself. I know it's hard when you are in pain to focus on positive thoughts and happiness. If you are having difficulty defining what you need and what makes you happy beyond "being pain free" or "having one good day," that's OK.

Perhaps daydreaming, remembering happiness or doing the "Five Imaginary Lives" or "Date Yourself" exercises will spur you on to explore new options for your healing.

For me, after years of suffering debilitating migraines, it was my desire to actually live one of my imaginary lives (rock star) that got me looking for alternative treatments.

An interesting event around pain and happiness happened to me recently. I was walking around thinking about how happy and loved I felt, how much I love living where I am and doing what I do, enjoying my dog and singing with my band. The next day, we had an afternoon gig, and it went really well. I was happy with our performance and the audience's reception to one of my original songs. I was driving home, reliving the good feelings of the day. I was very happy. And *WHAM*, my car was hit by another car. Yes, pain. The next day, I was walking my dog when I realized I was thinking "nobody loves me, everybody hates me, I think I'll eat some worms" thoughts. I called my good friend and doctor and told her how odd it was that nothing depression-worthy had happened. My life was the same, but today the negative thoughts were just inconsolable.

Her reply was, "The last time you were in this much pain, you were incredibly unhappy. Your brain jumped the tracks. It felt physical pain and said to itself, 'Oh, I know how to do this. Physical pain goes with these emotions and these thoughts.' That's why it makes no sense why you feel so emotional today when you were so blissful yesterday."

My task then was to be alert to my self-talk, and jump in and turn it around. Let me just say, that it was an exhausting multi-day task.

If you're in pain and you're doing this work for yourself, right on! You go! Woo hoo!

Resources

Here are resources I've found helpful on my journey.

Workshops

What Truly Matters

I've learned so much from Aimee Lyndon-Adams over the years; her wisdom was pivotal in moving my post-divorce despair into blazing happiness. She discusses energy and intention, how we can take responsibility and control of our energy and how we can deal with other people either "sucking" our energy or "dumping" on us!
http://bit.ly/whattrulymatters

Guided Meditations

I've created a series of guided mediations to help you with many of the sections of this book. The guided meditations include

- *Getting Started – Mediation Made Easy*
- *Finding a Quiet Space in Your Mind*
- *Getting Unstuck*
- *Releasing Fear*

www.happiness-handbook.com

Books and Movies

The Artist's Way by Julia Cameron. Tarcher, 2002. Offers many wonderful exercises for unblocking your creativity. It's not just for artists that hold a brush; it's for anyone yearning to live a richer, creative life. Available on Amazon.

Creative Visualization by Shakti Gawain. New World Press, 2002. Harnesses the power of your mind to help you determine what you want and bring it into your life. If seeing is believing, then see it first in your mind's eye. Available on Amazon.

Hiring the Heavens by Jean Slatter. New World Library, 2005. A quick, easy read about asking for help, hiring the right team, defining the tasks and letting your heavenly team pitch in. Does this mean that you can sit back and wait? Of course not; you still need to take action here on earth to make your dreams come true, but a little support from the sweet angels on the other side never hurt! Available on Amazon.

Loving Yourself by Aimee Lyndon-Adams is the book that helped me start healing when I was at my most messed up and unhappy. It was instrumental in helping me get back to neutral. Available only at: http://bit.ly/whattrulymatters

What The Bleep DVD by Betsy Chasse. 20th Century Fox, 2005. I found this movie very interesting. It brings together quantum physicists, educators and Meta-physicists and bridges the gap about how the brain works. The documentary-style movie has a storyline and animation. Available on Amazon.

The Secret produced by Rhonda Byrne. Prime Time Productions, 2006. The next logical step after _What The Bleep_ discusses more about how your mind works and the power of the law of attraction. It's been discussed on _The Oprah Winfrey Show_ and _Larry King Live_. Available on Amazon and Amazon Instant.

About The Author

Jenn began life immersed in the arts but took a detour in college and began her career doing software testing at NASA in Maryland. NASA had the good sense to send her on a business trip to California and, during a weekend sight-seeing trip, she realized Marin County was her home. After moving to the Bay Area and doing a couple stints at high-tech startups, she started her own companies, Vettanna (high-tech staffing and strategic communications) and Vettanna ToGo (on-camera training).

Upon post-divorce reflection, Jenn's creative and artist side re-emerged. Kind of like Dr. Jekyll and Ms Hyde (if Hyde can be a rocker chick/song writer/author instead of a lunatic!)

Jenn lives in Marin County with Miss Sophie, her dog. She's still the visionary for Vettanna and is the lead singer for her band, Urban Fiction.

"Rock on 'lil mama"

Photo by Lori Fuller Photography

Staying in Touch

Read the blogs:

www.happiness-handbook.com

www.betterboyfriend.net

Hang out on Facebook:

https://www.facebook.com/HappinessHandbook

Rock Out with the Band:

https://www.facebook.com/UrbanFiction

Index

How I Use This Book   **19**
Overcoming Heartbreak   19
The Top 5 Deal Breakers   20
Trouble Spots and Red Flags   20
The Action of "Being" Happy   21

What I Know for Sure—About Men   **23**
What That Means for Us Chicas   23
The One Thing I Want You to Know   23

The Road to Happiness   **27**
A Word on Terminology   27
The 3 Steps of Happiness   28
Step 1: Decide What Makes You Happy   29
The Happiness Deficit   29
Forgiveness   30
Defining Happiness in Terms of Others   31
The Happiness Layer Cake   32
Step 2: Communicating What Makes You Happy   34
What I Know for Sure—Mind Reading   34
Hints   34
Timing is Everything   35
Rule 1: Don't Overwhelm   35
Rule 2: Watch the Focus   36
Rule 3: It's in His Eyes   37
Are You Mystery Dating?   38
Are You in a Relationship?   38
Communicating with Family and Friends   38
Step 3: Happy Dance   39
The Face of Happiness   39
Happiness as Manipulation   41

An Experiment 42

How to Figure Out What Makes You Happy 45

Techniques for Figuring Out What Makes You Happy 45
Meditation 45
Free Association Writing 46
Brainstorm 47
Walking 47
Reminisce and Fantasize 47
Opposites 48
Organizing Your Happiness Lists 49
Random Order or Priority Order? 49
Add Your Stories 49

What Makes Me Happy 51

What Makes Me Happy—The Top 5 Must Haves 53
What Happiness Looks Like On Me 55
The Things You Do that Make Me Happy 57
The Things We Do Together that Makes Me Happy 59
What Makes Me Serene 61
What I Do For You That Makes Me Happy 63

What Makes Me Tick 65

What I Provide 66
What I Need 67
What I Need 68
Respect 71
What Makes Me Feel Respected 73
Frivolous Facts—Just For Fun! 75
Dates I'd Like to Go On 77
Presents I Like 79
Favorite "Cheats" 81
I Really Don't Like 83
When I'm Sick 85

Freaking Out   87
When I'm Emotional and It's Not About You   87
When I'm Emotional and You're Involved   89

Who You (My Happiness Bringer) Are   91
Chocolate Receiver and Olive Bringer   92
Who You (My Happiness Bringer) Are   93
Top 5 Deal Breakers   95

Sex   97
Answers to the Top 8 Questions   98
The Spots that Do Me   99
Signs I'm "In the Mood"   101
What I'd Like to Do to You   103
The Perfect Moment Below the Belt   105
The Perfect "After"   107
More Information, Stories and Fantasies   109

The Dark Side   111
What Bugs Me   112
Big Deals   114
Receiving Feedback   116
The Dark Side — Bad Habits that Just Are   118

Living an Extraordinary Life   121
My Extraordinary Life   123

Life Purpose   125

Troubleshooting   127
Defining Happiness   127
Five Imaginary Lives   127
Date Yourself   128
Vision Board/Collage   129
Guided Meditations   129
Fears   129

A New Outcome   130
Fear of Revealing Yourself   131
1. An Exercise   131
2. Lock It Up   131
3. Get Over It   132
Getting Unstuck or Getting to Neutral   132
Making Space   132
Fire Them or Set Them Free   133
Cut the Link   134
Pretend   135
Moving   136
Clear the Anger   138
The Chair   138
At Bat   139
Plates   140
Sorrow or Anger in 5 Minutes/Day   140
Accountability   141
Play   143
Diet   143
Tips for Getting Off Sugar or Chocolate   144
Receiving   145
A Glass of Water   145
Reframing the Offer   146
Dinner   147
The Power of Your Mind   147
Positive Reinforcement   147
Rewiring   147
Physical Pain   148

Resources   **151**
Workshops   151
Guided Meditations   151
Books and Movies   152

Staying in Touch   **154**

12902976R00084